Kipper Tells the Time

Written by Roderick Hunt

Illustrated by Alex Brychta

8 am

eight o'clock

Kipper woke up at eight o'clock.

"Hooray," he said. "It's Saturday."

9 am

At nine o’clock, Kipper painted a picture of Mum.

“It looks just like her,” said Dad.

10 am

At ten o'clock, the whole family went to the playground.

"I love the swings," said Kipper.

11 am

At eleven o'clock, Mum took Biff, Chip and Kipper to the swimming pool.

2.30 pm

Half past two

At two-thirty, Mum took the children to watch Dad play football.

"Come on, Dad!" called Chip.

5.45 pm

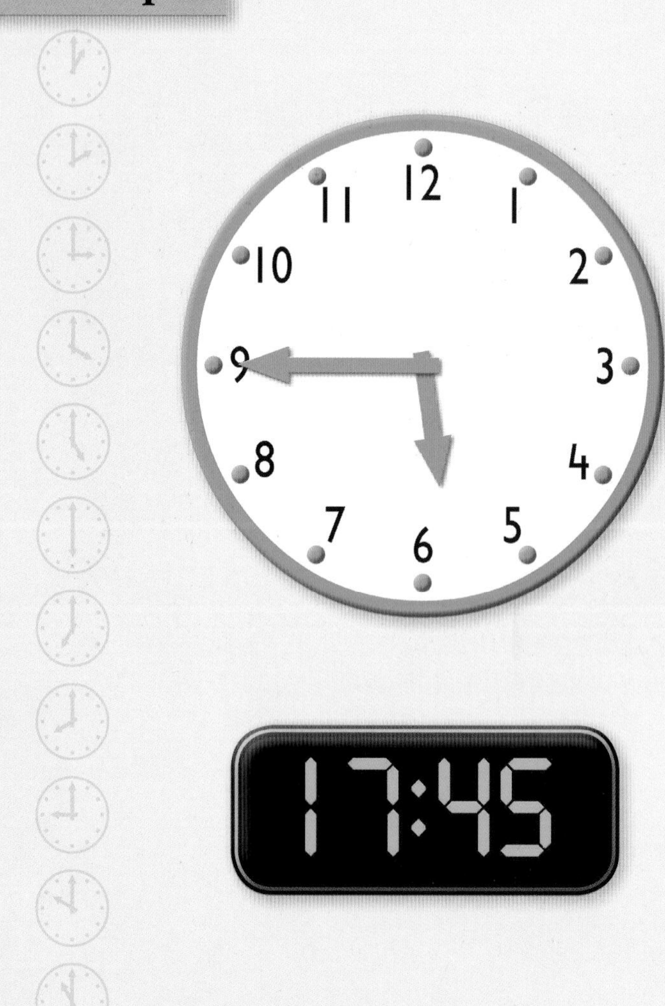

A quarter to six

At a quarter to six, the children watched television. It was their favourite programme.

7.15 pm

A quarter past seven

At a quarter past seven, Kipper got ready for bed. He put on his pyjamas and cleaned his teeth.

What time is it?

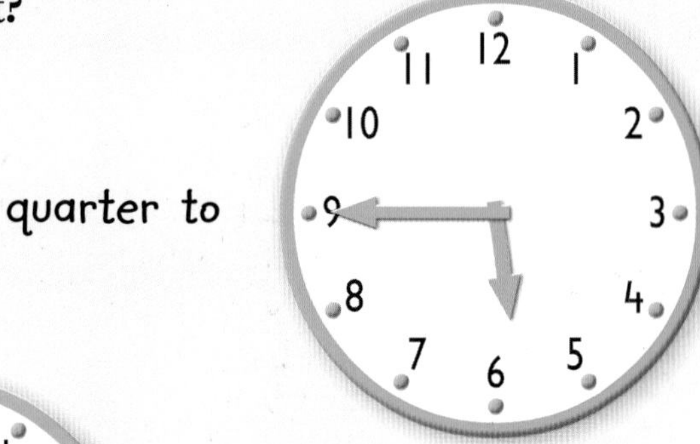

quarter to

quarter past

half past

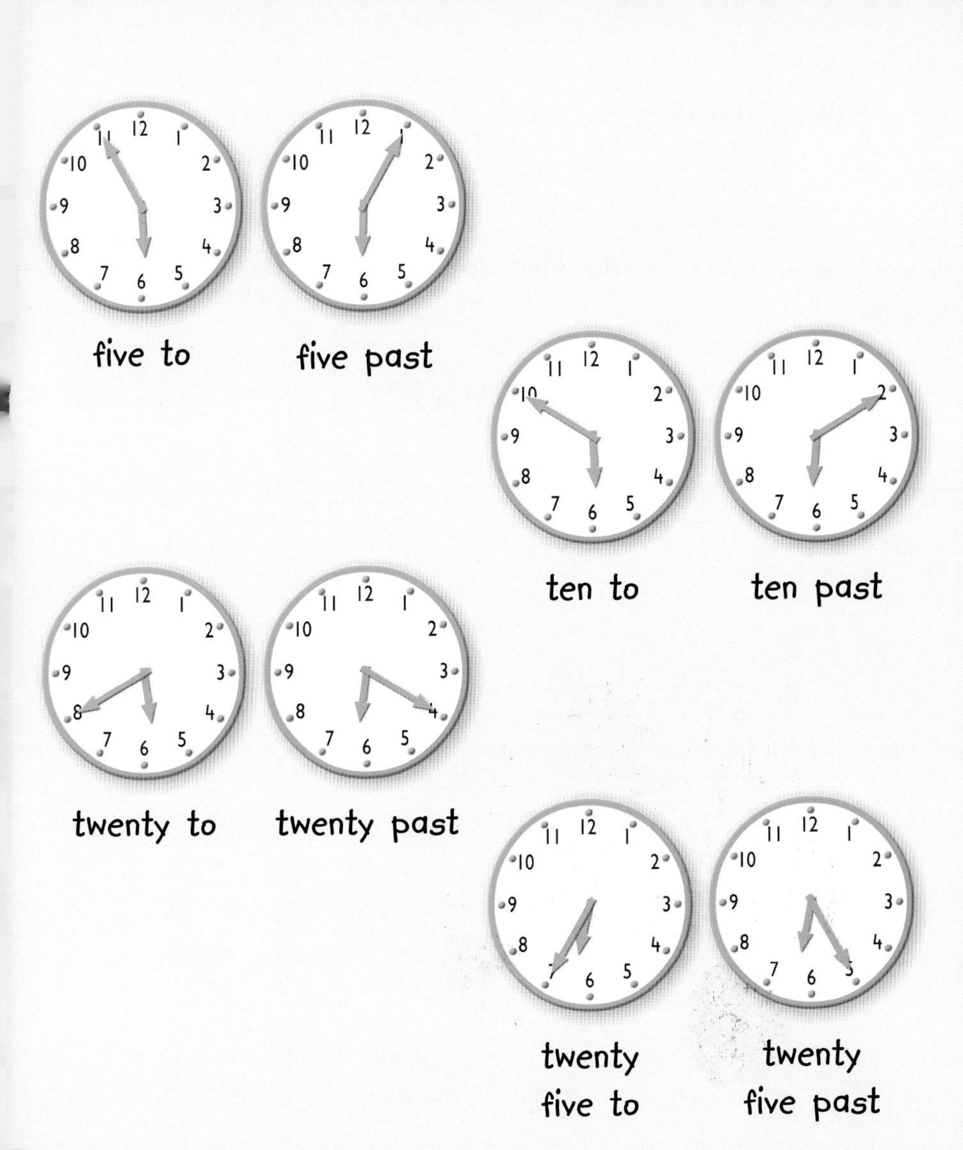
five to
five past
ten to
ten past
twenty to
twenty past
twenty five to
twenty five past

Kipper's day

What time did
Kipper wake up?

What time did
he go swimming?

What time did
Kipper watch TV?

What time did
he go to bed?

Talk about time

What has hands and a face but no arms or legs?

What did the family do on Saturday afternoon?

What time do you go to bed on Saturdays?

What do you like to do on Saturdays?